JOHN MUELLER

OINK

HEAVEN'S BUTCHER

NORTHAMPTON KITCHEN SINK PRESS *MASSACHUSETTS*

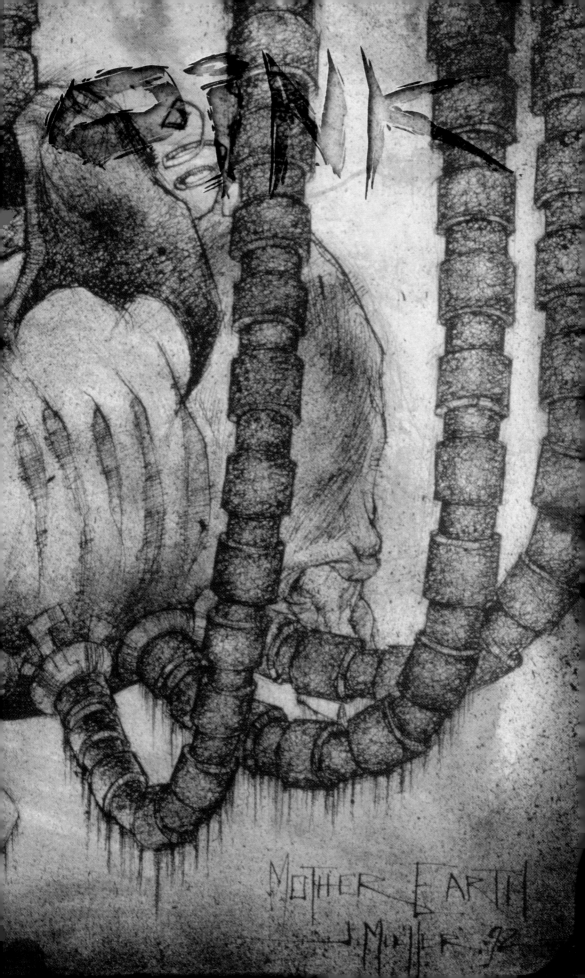

MOTHER EARTH

J. MULLER 92

All my great memories
the ones of bright light
through fuzzy glass I owe
       to them
Martha and Buzy
    this one's for you

Come one come all
Welcome to the wonderful world of Slaughterhouse Sins
and crimson dreams
Home to the infamous flying pigs
the ones you have all heard about
Watch them fly freely
as if they always were
and always will be
Through the door straight to hell
When you hear the dinner bell
a meat wagon for you a meat wagon for me
We will ride the corridors of this ancient machine together
Welcome to this fun house
Carousels of cadavers with common names
spin endlessly on pins of splintered bone
Dash your hopes
release your screams
Support the ceiling with filthy dreams
Nothing is as it seems
don't be afraid to throw off your skin
and dance around in your bones
Some blood and circus in this city of loons
that's what we all need
beware the butcher
for he roams this labyrinth
of coffin-like lockers and blood streaked floors
take heed and take care
Just a few more seers

you're almost there

BIG
PIG
INK

"To the future or to the past, to a time when thought is free,
when men are different from one another and do not live alone—
to a time when truth exists and what is done cannot be undone:
From the age of uniformity, from the age of solitude, from the age
of Big Brother, from the age of doublethink—greetings!"

—*George Orwell, 1984*

IT BE DONE...

MY TIME OF DYING DRAWS NEAR

THE BUCKETS OF BLOOD WHICH I HAVE SPILT FROM MY ENEMIES HAS CREATED AN OCEAN THAT I MUST NOW CROSS IN THE BOAT I HAVE BUILT FROM THEIR BONES.

MY SAILS ARE SEWN FROM THEIR SKIN...

..THE WIND WHICH FILLS THEM ARE THEIR LAST BREATHS..

... I WILL STARE OUT INTO THIS OCEAN OF DEATH AND TELL IT THE TALE OF MY BEGINNING SO THAT I MAY FIND MERCY IN THE END.

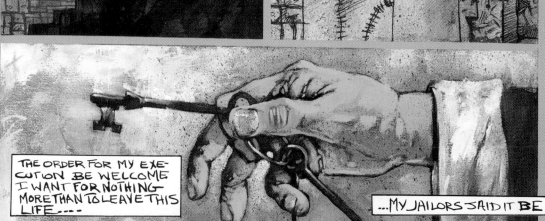

THE ORDER FOR MY EXECUTION BE WELCOME I WANT FOR NOTHING MORE THAN TO LEAVE THIS LIFE....

...MY JAILORS SAID IT BE

THEY SEND A CHILD OUT TO FACE THE STORM.

..THE MERCIFUL SLAUGHTER OF A LUNATIC.

..WELL, BOY, HERE I BE... THE STORM.

I BE OINK AND YOU BE HERE TO TAKE DOWN THE LAST WORDS SPOKEN FROM THIS THROAT.

YES, Q43 ....I.. UH.. MEAN OINK ..I BROUGHT A SCRIBE AS YOU REQUESTED.

YOUR EXECUTION WILL BE HELD AT FIRST LIGHT TOMORROW.

TAP TAP TAP

Chapter 1
AWAKENINGS

ANOTHER DAY WOULD BEGIN...

...ANOTHER OPPORTUNITY TO PROVIDE A BIT OF GREASE FOR THE RUSTED GEARS OF HEAVEN...

...THE PARADISE WHERE ANGELS DWELL...

...AND RESTLESS SOULS CAN FIND SALVATION IN...

... THE SAVIOUR'S ARMS.
DA' WORDS IN MY HEAD WERE NEW TO ME...
...DEY' BE THOUGHTS...
I BE NOT ALLOWED TO HAVE DESE!...
I KNOW WHY NOW.
THEY....
PUBLIC SLAUGHTERHOUSE 628
NO TRESPASSING NO LOITERING
...COMPLICATE THINGS.

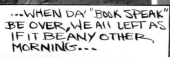

...WHEN DA' "BOOK SPEAK" BE OVER, WE All LEFT AS IF IT BE ANY OTHER MORNING...

I KNOW YOU AND SPIGOT WERE FRIENDS, OINK. YOU MUST BE-WARE OF THE EVILS WHICH CORRUPTED HIS SPIRIT.

HE SHALL BE MISSED. IT IS A GRIEVOUS LOSS.

YES IT BE, WARDEN.

"THE GOOD ONE" HAS SPOKEN OUT TO ME FROM ON HIGH! THE GOODNESS OF HIS HOUSE HAS BEEN PRESERVED!

DEY' CHAIN US UP...

...NO I CHAIN ME UP...

...WHERE DEY' TINK' OINK GONNA' GO...HEAVEN?

HEAVEN??...

WARDEN SAY IT'S A BEAUTIFUL PLACE AII FILLED UP WIT' ANGELS...

HE SAY WE CAN'T GO DERE, BUT DAT WE SERVE IT. DAT' USED TA' MAKE ME FEEL GOOD.

OTHER DAY DONE, ODY SPEAKS, NO-SAY NUTHIN' BOUT' HIN'. WE JUS' SLEEP O IT AII OVER AGAIN. OT SAID IT AII BE S." I DON' ONDERSTAND T', BUT DEY KILT HIM FOR IT.

...NOT NO MORE... DEY' KILT SPIGOT.

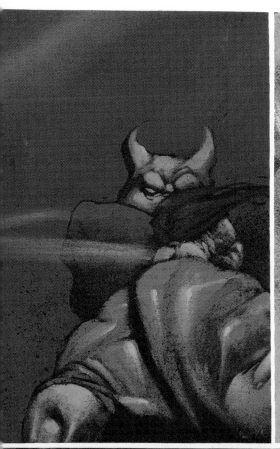
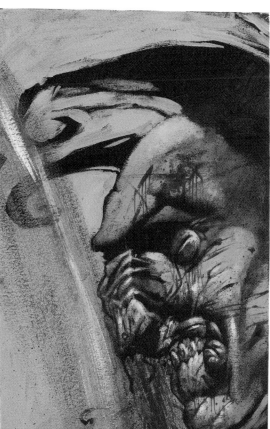

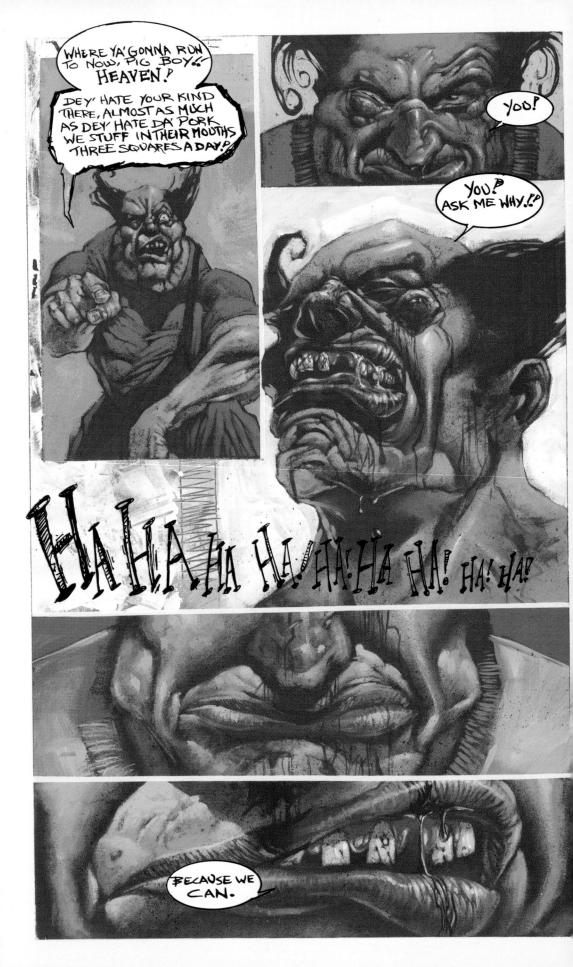

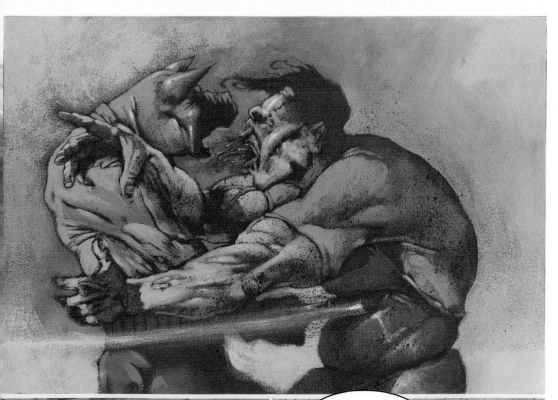

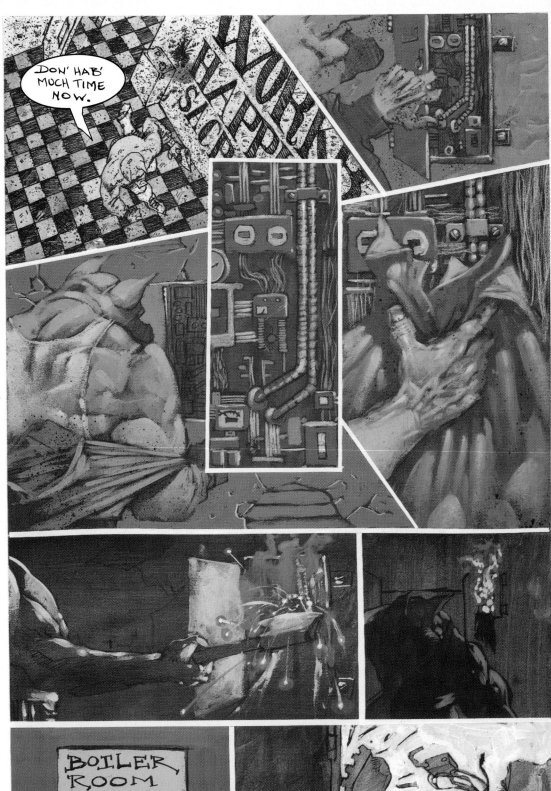

HEAVEN

MMPH... NOT SAFE YET.. NNNYA...

GOT TA'.. G FAR NUFF

...AWA

GOT TA' RUN...

Chapter 2
LIES

HE SHALL BE DEAD BY DAWN, MY CARDINAL!
YOU ARE MY ANGELS OF MERCY. SHOW THIS PIG NONE!!!

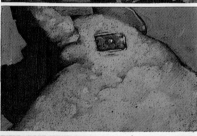

Chapter 3
TRUTHS

PIG

MAN

I WASN'T SURE I STILL HAD IT IN ME, BUT LIKE A CYCLE ONE NEVER FORGETS, EVEN WITHOUT MY EYE'S.
MY NAME IS MARY, DEAR. THIS IS MY GRANDSON HERBERT WE WELCOME YOUR COMPANY.
DO YOU HAVE A NAME?

Chapter 4
PIGS

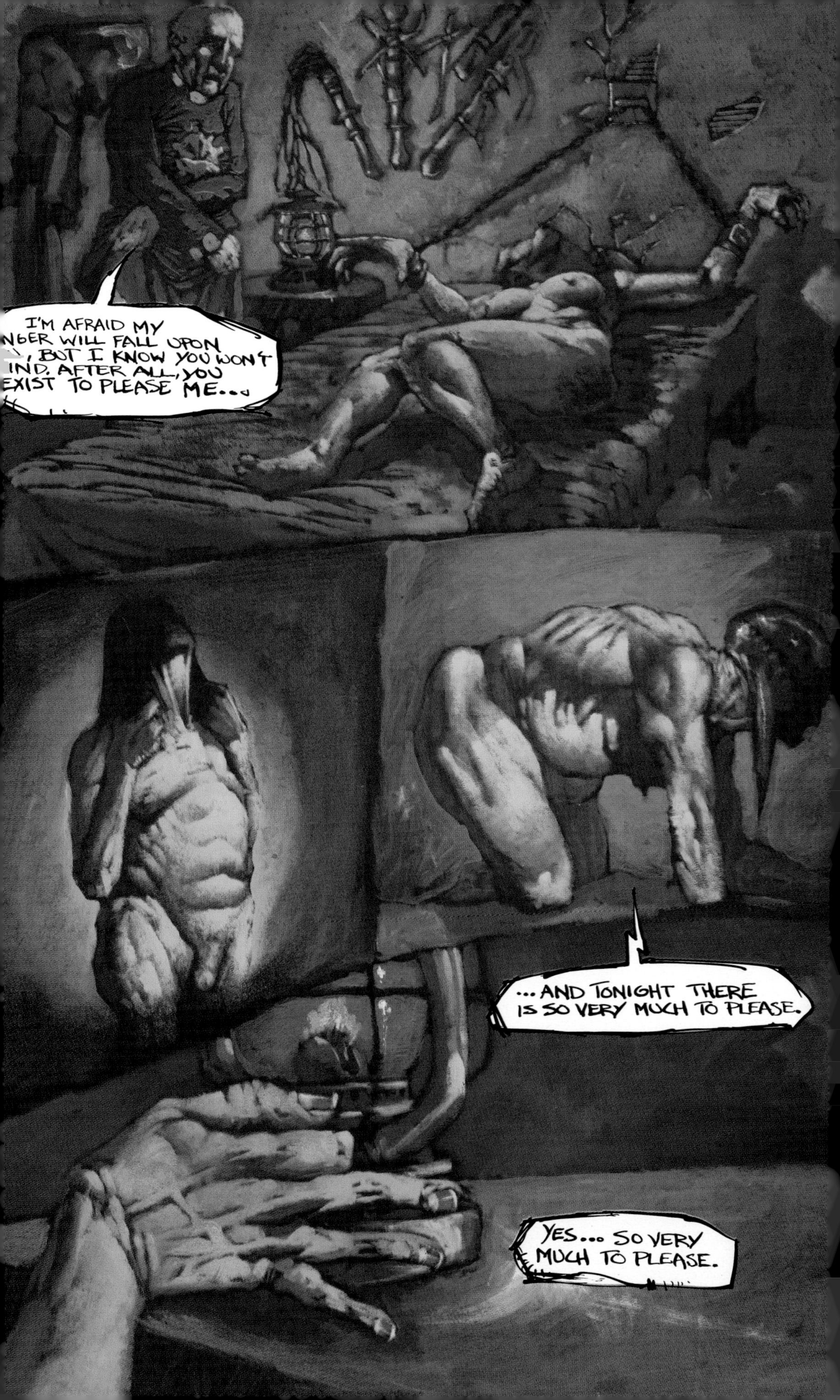
I'M AFRAID MY
NGER WILL FALL UPON
, BUT I KNOW YOU WON'T
IND. AFTER ALL, YOU
EXIST TO PLEASE ME...
...AND TONIGHT THERE IS SO VERY MUCH TO PLEASE.
YES... SO VERY MUCH TO PLEASE.

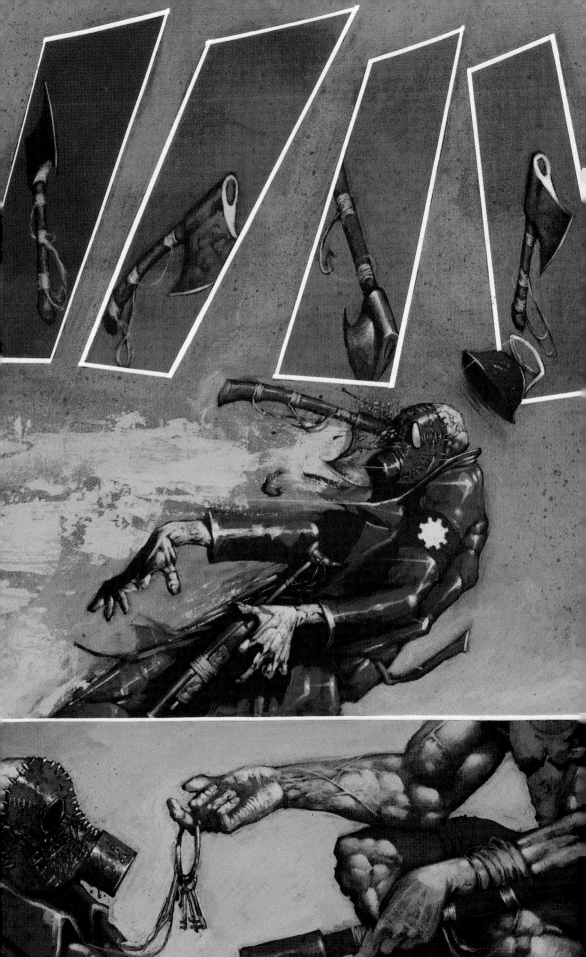

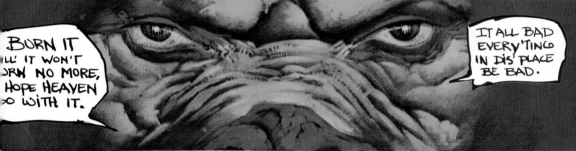

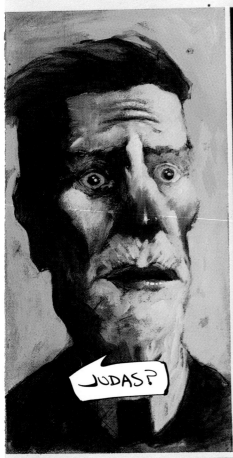

JUDAS?

...AND LO, THE DEMON WALKED IN THE LAND OF THE LIVING HIS BODY CAKED WIT THE BLOOD OF THOSE WHO HAD WRONGE HIM.

...AND THE DEMON PRESSED HIS DRIED AND CRACKED LIPS TO THE POOL OF MAN TO DRINK HIS FILL, AND HIS THIRST WAS SATED...

...MAY THE SAVIOR FIND MERCY IN HIS HEART FOR US.

HERBERT, I BE
SORRY.

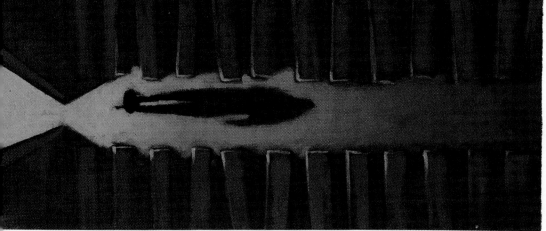

BACAAR! I COME FOR YOU!

AH! YOU MUST BE THE UNRULY PIG I HAVE HEARD SO MUCH ABOUT, BURNING BUILDINGS, KILLING ANGELS, COMMITING All SORTS OF HEINOUS ACTS.

I BE HIM.

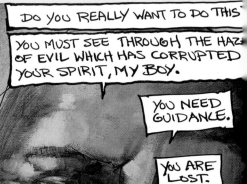

DO YOU REALLY WANT TO DO THIS?

YOU MUST SEE THROUGH THE HAZE OF EVIL WHICH HAS CORRUPTED YOUR SPIRIT, MY BOY.

YOU NEED GUIDANCE.

YOU ARE LOST.

LOOK AT THE RE[ST] OF YOUR KIND THEY STAND IN LINE AND SIT [IN] ROWS, AND AR[E] HAPPY TO DO S[O].

I CAN HELP Y[OU] FIND YOUR W[AY] BACK.

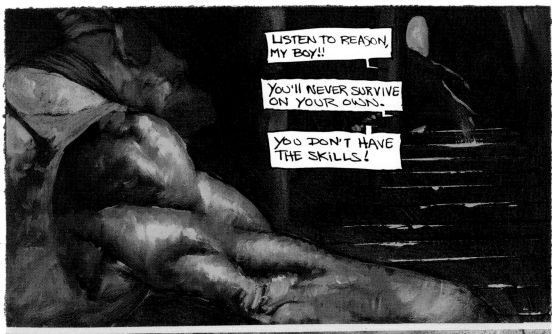

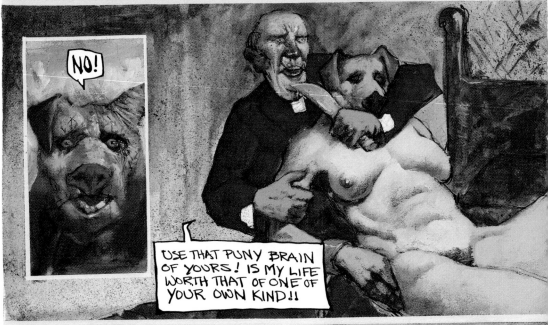

THE GEARS WHICH HAD GROUND SO MANY TO DUST HAD FINALLY SPUTTERED AND STOPPED.

YOU WONDER IF I GRASP THE MAGNITUDE OF MY SINS, BOY?

FOR DAYS I WATCHED HEAVEN BURN. AND AS THE LAST BRICK FELL FROM ITS ONCE LOFTY PERCH, I UNDERSTOOD THE NECESSITY OF DA' SLAUGHTER.

I BURNED AND SLAUGHTERED THOUSANDS DAT DAY. AND OVER DA' REST OF MY LIFE THOUSANDS MORE.

DERE' CRIES FOR MERCY ELL ON DEAF EARS.

I BECAME DA' JUDGEMENT, AND IN DA' END, DERE' GOD. RUTHLESS AND UNFALTERING IN MY CRUELTY.

AGAINST ALL DA' LAWS OF NATURE, MAN CREATED ME.

I HAVE NO GRATITUDE FOR DAT'. ONLY AN ENDLESS WELL OF ANGER FROM WHICH TO DRAW MY ENTIRE LIFE.

JM96

EPILOGUE

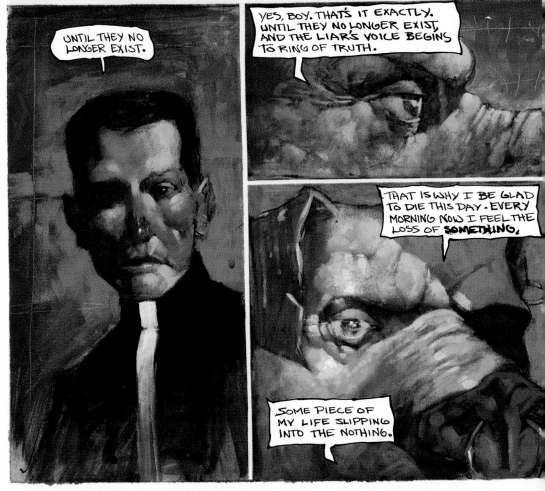

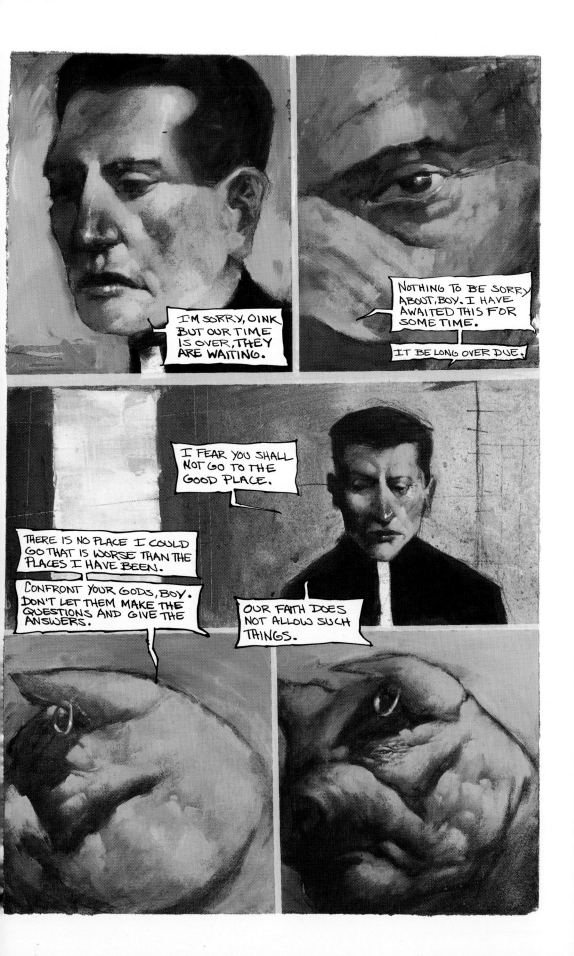

"Here they come {Los Bastardos}"

This painting was the key to the Pandora's box that Oink has become. I did this back in 1992 or 1991. It took me a solid month—12 hrs. a day. It was also my first painting. By that I mean it was my first piece that showed any understanding of composition, color and execution. It set the groundwork for the Oink series. And during the making of Oink I would often refer back to it.

Cover art for Oink #1, published December 1995.

Cover art for Oink #2, published February 1996.

Cover art for Oink #3, published April 1996.

Mary, an all-around fun character to write and draw.

HERBERT 1,

8'TALL

Herbert, the big lummox. I hated killing him.

Cardinal Bacaar, or as he was known at the time, Bagone.
Finding a suitable look and title for this fellow took some time. This was the
second look he had, which I later decided was entirely too evil.

This page was one of the original seven that I did to pitch the project.

OINK
BLOOD & CIRCUS

Out with the old and in with the new. The next series will throw Oink in with a whole new cast of characters—with a post-Apocalyptic circus and freak show as the backdrop.